Rhymes for All Seasons

A Collection of Countryside Poems

Selected by Jane Asher

Illustrated by Jenny Partridge

DEAN

First published 1994 by Dean
an imprint of Reed Consumer Books Ltd
Michelin House, 81 Fulham Road, London SW3 6RB
and Auckland, Melbourne, Singapore and Toronto

ISBN 0 603 55582 9

Produced by Mandarin

Printed and bound in Hong Kong

To the children who will read this book

It is odd to think that human beings are capable of producing such extremes of beauty and horror. We can create extraordinarily moving and truthful poetry, art and music, but at the same time we blindly devise more and more effective ways of destroying life on our planet.

You and your friends, like every new generation, will have the chance to save what is good and to right the wrongs you inherit, but it won't be easy. It never is easy to change things. You will have to battle not only with powerful forces in society but also with yourself because it is always more comfortable to opt for a quiet life rather than risking standing up for what you believe in. And it is especially difficult when you are bombarded from all sides with the temptation to live ever more materialistic and acquisitive lives.

That's why I love these poems. They appeal directly to the part of us that is beyond the everyday and touch something universal in us – an instinctive yearning for truth and beauty. Some of the poems do this by reminding us just how wonderful the world is, some by making us laugh, others by shocking us into seeing what we are doing to our environment. Perhaps some of you have not yet had the chance to enjoy the gentle country world of some of the poems, but beauty is to be found everywhere – even in a blade of grass sticking up through the cracks in the pavement – and I hope this book will help you see it.

Some of the poems in this collection are ones I have enjoyed since childhood, others are more recent discoveries, and a few are completely new and written by your contemporaries. Enjoy reading them and looking at the beautiful illustrations; have happy lives on this magical planet; and forgive us – the adults – for leaving your inheritance in such an endangered state.

JANE ASHER

Ode to the Ozone

Aerosols are quite appalling,
One quick spray,
Twice a day,
Whoops, the ozone's falling.

North Sea seals are slowly sinking,
Caked with mud,
Choked on blood,
Just because we're not thinking.

Poison petrol pollutes the planet,
Too much lead,
Brain dead,
If it isn't lead free – ban it!

HUGH TALLENTS
(aged 8)

The Seasons

Four Seasons

Spring is showery, flowery, bowery.
Summer: hoppy, choppy, poppy.
Autumn: wheezy, sneezy, freezy.
Winter: slippy, drippy, nippy.

ANON

The Months

January brings the snow,
Makes our feet and fingers glow.

February brings the rain,
Thaws the frozen lake again.

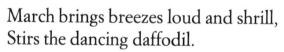

March brings breezes loud and shrill,
Stirs the dancing daffodil.

April brings the primrose sweet,
Scatters daisies at our feet.

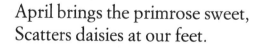

The Seasons

May brings flocks of pretty lambs,
Skipping by their fleecy dams.

June brings tulips, lilies, roses,
Fills the children's hands with posies.

Hot July brings cooling showers,
Apricots and gillyflowers.

August brings the sheaves of corn,
Then the harvest home is borne.

Warm September brings the fruit,
Sportsmen then begin to shoot.

Fresh October brings the pheasant,
Then to gather nuts is pleasant.

Dull November brings the blast,
Then the leaves are whirling fast.

Chill December brings the sleet,
Blazing fire, and Christmas treat.

SARA COLERIDGE

Spring Song

from PIPPA PASSES

The year's at the spring
And day's at the morn;
Morning's at seven;
The hillside's dew-pearled;
The lark's on the wing;
The snail's on the thorn;
God's in his heaven—
All's right with the world!

ROBERT BROWNING

The Corn Growing

Snow no longer snowing,
Wind ends its blowing,
Every stream fresh flowing,
A cockerel loudly crowing,
New grass blades slowly showing,
A bullock deeply lowing,
The chilly evenings going,
And almost without knowing,
The corn growing.

LEONARD CLARK

Written in March

The cock is crowing,
The stream is flowing,
The small birds twitter,
The lake doth glitter,
The green field sleeps in the sun;
The oldest and youngest
Are at work with the strongest;
The cattle are grazing,
Their heads never raising;
There are forty feeding like one!

Like an army defeated
The snow hath retreated,
And now doth fare ill
On the top of the bare hill;
The ploughboy is whooping – anon – anon:
There's joy in the mountains;
There's life in the fountains;
Small clouds are sailing,
Blue sky prevailing;
The rain is over and gone!

WILLIAM WORDSWORTH

The Scarecrow

All winter through I bow my head
  Beneath the driving rain;
The North Wind powders me with snow
  And blows me black again;
At midnight in a maze of stars
  I flame with glittering rime,
And stand, above the stubble, stiff
  As mail at morning-prime.
But when that child, called Spring, and all
  His host of children, come,
Scattering their buds and dew upon
  These acres of my home,
Some rapture in my rags awakes;
  I lift void eyes and scan
The skies for crows, those ravening foes,
  Of my strange master, Man.
I watch him striding lank behind
  His clashing team, and know
Soon will the wheat swish body high
  Where once lay sterile snow;
Soon shall I gaze across a sea
  Of sun-begotten grain,
Which my unflinching watch hath sealed
  For harvest once again.

WALTER DE LA MARE

Adlestrop

Yes, I remember Adlestrop—
The name, because one afternoon
Of heat the express-train drew up there
Unwontedly. It was late June.

The steam hissed. Someone cleared his throat.
No one left and no one came
On the bare platform. What I saw
Was Adlestrop – only the name.

And willows, willow-herb, and grass,
And meadowsweet, and haycocks dry,
No whit less still and lonely fair
Than the high cloudlets in the sky.

And for that minute a blackbird sang
Close by, and round him, mistier,
Farther and farther, all the birds
Of Oxfordshire and Gloucestershire.

Edward Thomas

September

The golden-rod is yellow,
　The corn is turning brown;
The trees in apple orchards
　With fruit are bending down.

The gentian's bluest fringes
　Are curling in the sun;
In dusty pods the milkweed
　Its hidden silk has spun.

The sedges flaunt their harvest,
　In every meadow-nook;
And asters by the brookside
　Make asters in the brook.

By all these lovely tokens
　September days are here,
With summer's best of wealth
　And autumn's best of cheer.

HELEN HUNT JACKSON

Snow

The snow fell softly all the night.
It made a blanket soft and white.
It covered houses, flowers and ground,
But did not make a single sound!

ALICE WILKINS

The Seasons

Stopping by Woods on a Snowy Evening

Whose woods these are I think I know.
His house is in the village though;
He will not see me stopping here
To watch his woods fill up with snow.

My little horse must think it queer
To stop without a farmhouse near
Between the woods and frozen lake
The darkest evening of the year.

He gives his harness bells a shake
To ask if there is some mistake.
The only other sound's the sweep
Of easy wind and downy flake.

The woods are lovely, dark and deep,
But I have promises to keep,
And miles to go before I sleep,
And miles to go before I sleep.

ROBERT FROST

The Earth

The Poem

It is only a little twig
With a green bud at the end;
But if you plant it,
And water it,
And set it where the sun will be above it,
It will grow into a tall bush
With many flowers,
And leaves which thrust hither and thither
Sparkling.
From its roots will come freshness,
And beneath it the grass-blades
Will bend and recover themselves,
And clash one upon another
In the blowing wind.

But if you take my twig
And throw it into a closet
With mousetraps and blunted tools,
It will shrivel and waste.
And, some day,
When you open the door,
You will think it an old twisted nail,
And sweep it into the dust bin
With other rubbish.

AMY LOWELL

Under Ground

In the deep kingdom under ground
There is no light and little sound.

Down below the earth's green floor
The rabbit and the mole explore.

The quarrying ants run to and fro
To make their populous empires grow.

Do they, as I pass overhead,
Stop in their work to hear my tread?

Some creatures sleep and do not toil,
Secure and warm beneath the soil.

Sometimes a fork or spade intrudes
Upon their earthy solitudes.

Downward the branching tree-roots spread
Into the country of the dead.

Deep down, the buried rocks and stones
Are like the earth's gigantic bones.

In the dark kingdom under ground
How many marvellous things are found!

JAMES REEVES

The Earth

Nettles

My son aged three fell in the nettle bed.
'Bed' seemed a curious name for those green spears,
That regiment of spite behind the shed:
It was no place for rest. With sobs and tears
The boy came seeking comfort and I saw
White blisters beaded on his tender skin.
We soothed him till his pain was not so raw.
At last he offered us a watery grin,
And then I took my hook and honed the blade
And went outside and slashed in fury with it
Till not a nettle in that fierce parade
Stood upright anymore. Next task: I lit
A funeral pyre to burn the fallen dead.
But in two weeks the busy sun and rain
Had called up tall recruits behind the shed:
My son would often feel sharp wounds again.

VERNON SCANNELL

Stupidity Street

I saw with open eyes
Singing birds sweet
Sold in the shops
For the people to eat,
Sold in the shops of
Stupidity Street.

I saw in vision
The worm in the wheat,
And in the shops nothing
For people to eat;
Nothing for sale in
Stupidity Street.

RALPH HODGSON

Trees

The Oak is called the king of trees,
The Aspen quivers in the breeze,
The Poplar grows up straight and tall,
The Peach tree spreads along the wall,
The Sycamore gives pleasant shade,
The Willow droops in watery glade,
The Fir tree useful timber gives,
The Beech amid the forest lives.

SARA COLERIDGE

The Earth

The Way through the Woods

They shut the road through the woods
Seventy years ago.
Weather and rain have undone it again
And now you would never know
There was once a road through the woods
Before they planted the trees.
It is underneath the coppice and heath
And the thin anemones.
Only the keeper sees
That, where the ring-dove broods,
And the badgers roll at ease,
There was once a road through the woods.

Yet, if you enter the woods
Of a summer evening late,
When the night air cools on the trout-ringed pools
Where the otter whistles his mate,
(They fear not man in the woods
Because they see so few),
You will hear the beat of a horse's feet,
And the swish of a skirt in the dew,
Steadily cantering through
The misty solitudes,
As though they perfectly knew
The old lost road through the woods. . .
But there is no road through the woods!

RUDYARD KIPLING

Wood-Strawberries

I went to the wood where the strawberries grow,
   And picked till my hands were red.
The grass was cool and the sun came warm
   Through the branches overhead.

Berry to berry beckoned me,
   Pointed and wild and sweet;
It seemed there was nothing to do at all
   But fill my hands and eat.

Nothing but greenness under foot,
   Greenery overhead,
And jewel-bright under their scalloped leaves
   Wild wood-strawberries red.

RACHEL FIELD

The Earth

New Road

They have dug up half of Tinkers' Hollow,
Next week other gangs will follow,
We've heard that everything is planned
To drive a road through this good land
Where herds of cows have grazed for years
Jerseys and Herefords, heifers and steers.

The flowers I love will have to go,
And every landmark that I know,
The secret summer places where
I walked alone in scented air,
The little lines of hawthorn trees
With hidden nests and swarms of bees.

Who wants a dangerous motorway
For all the motorists have to say,
With all the lorries rumbling by
Beneath a different country sky?

LEONARD CLARK

The Sea and the Shore

The Distance

Over the sounding sea,
Off the wandering sea
I smelt the smell of the distance
And longed for another existence.
Smell of pineapple, maize, and myrrh,
Parrot-feather and monkey-fur,
    Brown spice,
    Blue ice,
Fields of tobacco and tea and rice,

    And soundless snows,
    And snowy cotton,
    Otto of rose
Incense in an ivory palace,
Jungle rivers rich and rotten,
    Slumbering valleys,
    Smouldering mountains,
    Rank morasses
    And frozen fountains,
Black molasses and purple wine,
Coral and pearl and tar and brine,
The smell of panther and polar-bear
    And leopard-lair
    And mermaid-hair
Came from the four-cornered distance,
And I longed for another existence.

ELEANOR FARJEON

Neither Out Far Nor In Deep

The people along the sand
All turn and look one way.
They turn their back on the land.
They look at the sea all day

   As long as it takes to pass
   A ship keeps raising its hull;
   The wetter ground like glass
   Reflects a standing gull.

   The land may vary more;
   But wherever the truth may be—
   The water comes ashore,
   And the people look at the sea.

   They cannot look out far.
   They cannot look in deep.
   But when was that ever a bar
   To any watch they keep?

ROBERT FROST

The Sea and the Shore

The Tides to me, The Tides to me

The tides to me, the tides to me
  come dancing up the sand:
when the waves break I lean to take
  each one by the hand.

The tides from me, the tides from me
  roll backward down the shore.
I do not mind, for I shall find
  a thousand and one more.

GEORGE BARKER

The Great Blue Whale

An enormous mouth has he,
like a great dark cavern in the sea.
In his mind, he swims through oceans greeny-blue.
Now he sees the icebergs
rising frozen from the sea;
bears and seals and penguins too.
Now he sees the bottom of ships passing.
Up he rises to the surface,
huge spouts of water flying skywards.
Down to the bottom – he dives;
as his tail whisks and foam
whips up to the sapphire surface,
he dreams,
And he waits, suspended from the ceiling;
children throw pennies on his tail.

FRANCESCA DIMPFL

The Sea and the Shore

Echoes

The sea laments
The livelong day,
Fringing its waste of sand;
Cries back the wind from the whispering shore—
No words I understand:

Yet echoes in my heart a voice,
As far, as near, as these—
The wind that weeps,
The solemn surge
Of strange and lonely seas.

WALTER DE LA MARE

The Heavens

Windy Nights

Whenever the moon and stars are set,
  Whenever the wind is high,
All night long in the dark and wet,
  A man goes riding by.
Late in the night when the fires are out,
Why does he gallop and gallop about?

Whenever the trees are crying aloud,
  And ships are tossed at sea,
By, on the highway, low and loud,
  By at the gallop goes he.
By at the gallop he goes, and then
By he comes back at the gallop again.

ROBERT LOUIS STEVENSON

Storm

They're at it again
the wind and the rain
It all started
when the wind
took the window
by the collar
and shook it
with all its might
Then the rain
butted in
What a din
they'll be at it all night
Serves them right
if they go home in the morning
and the sky won't let them in

Roger McGough

The Heavens

Rain

There are holes in the sky
   Where the rain gets in,
But they're ever so small
   That's why rain is thin.

SPIKE MILLIGAN

The Weather

What's the weather on about?
Why is the rain so down on us?
Why does the sun glare at us so?

Why does the hail dance so prettily?
Why is the snow such an overall?
Why is the wind such a tearaway?

Why is the mud so fond of our feet?
Why is the ice so keen to upset us?
Who does the weather think it is?

GAVIN EWART

The Stars at Night

Twinkle, twinkle, little star,
How I wonder what you are!
Up above the world so high,
Like a diamond in the sky.

In the dark blue sky you keep
And often through my curtain peep,
For you never shut your eye
Till the sun is in the sky.

As your bright and tiny spark
Lights the traveller in the dark,
Though I know not what you are,
Twinkle, twinkle, little star.

Jane Taylor

The Heavens

Silver

Slowly, silently, now the moon
Walks the night in her silver shoon;
This way, and that, she peers, and sees
Silver fruit upon silver trees;
One by one the casements catch
Her beams beneath the silvery thatch;
Couched in his kennel, like a log,
With paws of silver sleeps the dog;
From their shadowing cote the white breasts peep
Of doves in a silver-feathered sleep;
A harvest mouse goes scampering by,
With silver claws, and silver eye;
And moveless fish in the water gleam,
By silver reeds in a silver stream.

WALTER DE LA MARE

The Budgie

The budgie has a bell to ring
And tunes from the radio to sing
A pot of water and pot of seed
For when he wants to drink or feed.
And every week a new sandsheet
To sharpen the claws of his bony feet.
He calls himself a pretty boy
But his only friend is a plastic toy.

Yet budgies fly in another land
Over miles of yellow sand
And peck the seeds that grow
And drink the streams that flow.
A crowd of uncaged budgies fly,
Green as grass or blue as sky.

Stanley Cook

The Heavens

Three Owls

Three owls were sitting in a tree,
Said one: "If two and one are three
And you are two as I can see
And we are three, then one is me!"
The other two said: "We agree."

RICHARD EDWARDS

The Swallow

Fly away, fly away, over the sea,
   Sun-loving swallow, for summer is done.
Come again, come again, come back to me,
   Bringing the summer and bringing the sun.

CHRISTINA ROSSETTI

Spiders and Flies and More Besides

The Fly

Little fly,
Thy summer's play
My thoughtless hand
Has brushed away.

Am not I
A fly like thee?
Or art not thou
A man like me?

For I dance
And drink and sing,
Till some blind hand
Shall brush my wing.

If thought is life
And strength and breath,
And the want
Of thought is death,

Then am I
A happy fly,
If I live
Or if I die.

WILLIAM BLAKE

Upside Down

It's funny how beetles
and creatures like that
can walk upside down
as well as walk flat:

They crawl on a ceiling
and climb on a wall
without any practice
or trouble at all,

While I have been trying
for a year (maybe more)
and still I can't stand
with my head on the floor.

AILEEN FISHER

Centipede

A centipede was happy quite,
    Until a frog in fun
Said, "Pray, which leg comes after which?"
This raised her mind to such a pitch,
She lay distracted in the ditch
    Considering how to run.

ANON

Spiders and Flies and More Besides

The Tickle Rhyme

"Who's that tickling my back?" said the wall.
"Me," said a small
Caterpillar. "I'm learning
To crawl."

IAN SERRAILLIER

The Butterfly in Church

Butterfly, butterfly, why come you here?
    This is no bower for you;
Go, sip the honey-drop sweet and clear,
    Or bathe in the morning dew.

This is the place to think of heaven,
    This is the place to pray;
You have no sins to be forgiven—
    Butterfly, go away!

WILLIAM COWPER

Silverfish, Spiders and Flies

Small creatures see
That none of the space
In our classroom
Goes to waste.

Silverfish keep warm
In cracks too small
Even for children's fingers
In the floor and against the wall.

And knitting their webs
The spiders fit
Onto ledges too narrow
For children to sit.

Flies stand on the ceiling
Or circle through the air
And even in P.E.
I never climbed up there.

Creatures that look
Like pips and seeds
Sow themselves in the places
No one else needs.

STANLEY COOK

If You Should Meet a Crocodile

If you should meet a crocodile,
   Don't take a stick and poke him;
Ignore the welcome in his smile,
   Be careful not to stroke him.
For as he sleeps upon the Nile,
   He thinner gets and thinner;
But whene'er you meet a crocodile
   He's ready for his dinner.

ANON

Snake Glides

Snake glides
   through grass
     over
       pebbles
        forked tongue
     working
   never
speaking
   but its
    body
      whispers
      listen

KEITH BOSLEY

44

Animals Large and Small

Pussy

I like little pussy, her coat is so warm;
And if I don't hurt her, she'll do me no harm.
So I'll not pull her tail, nor drive her away,
But pussy and I very gently will play.
She shall sit by my side, and I'll give her some food;
And she'll love me because I am gentle and good.

I'll pat pretty pussy, and then she will purr;
And thus show her thanks for my kindness to her.
But I'll not pinch her ears, nor tread on her paw,
Lest I should provoke her to use her sharp claw.
I never will vex her, nor make her displeased—
For pussy don't like to be worried and teased.

ANON

Mice

I think mice
Are rather nice

    Their tails are long,
    Their faces small,
    They haven't any
    Chins at all.
    Their ears are pink,
    Their teeth are white,
    They run about
    The house at night.
    They nibble things
    They shouldn't touch
    And no-one seems
    To like them much.

But I think mice
Are nice.

ROSE FYLEMAN

Dappled Grey

I had a little horse,
　　His name was Dappled Grey,
His head was made of gingerbread,
　　His tail was made of hay:
He could amble, he could trot,
　　He could carry the mustard pot,
He could amble, he could trot,
　　Through the old town of Windsor.

ANON

The Cow

The friendly cow, all red and white,
　　I love with all my heart:
She gives me cream with all her might,
　　To eat with apple-tart.

She wanders lowing here and there,
　　And yet she cannot stray,
All in the pleasant open air,
　　The pleasant light of day;

And blown by all the winds that pass
　　And wet with all the showers,
She walks among the meadow grass
　　And eats the meadow flowers.

ROBERT LOUIS STEVENSON

Ducks' Ditty

All along the backwater,
Through the rushes tall,
Ducks are a-dabbling,
Up tails all!

Ducks' tails, drakes' tails,
Yellow feet a-quiver,
Yellow bills all out of sight
Busy in the river!

Slushy green undergrowth
Where the roach swim—
Here we keep our larder,
Cool and full and dim.

Everyone for what he likes!
We like to be
Heads down, tails up,
Dabbling free!

High in the blue above
Swifts whirl and call—
We are down a-dabbling,
Up tails all!

KENNETH GRAHAME

Prayers

Pray for the millions of battery hens
confined in cramped cages and pens,
and for veal calves just staring at walls,
litters of pigs trapped in sour-smelling stalls.

The hens cannot spread even a single wing,
see the clear light from morning to evening,
stand with dulled feathers and pale flesh
on slopes of uncomfortable wire mesh.

Pray more for those who keep wide awake
all those miserable pigs and make
it impossible for them to turn around
and have to sleep on concreted ground.

Pray most for those who unthinkingly eat
any of their prison eggs and meat.

LEONARD CLARK

The Lamb

Little lamb, who made thee?
    Dost thou know who made thee,
Gave thee life, and made thee feed
By the stream and o'er the mead?
Gave thee clothing of delight,
Softest clothing, woolly, bright?
Gave thee such a tender voice,
Making all the vales rejoice?
    Little lamb, who made thee?
    Dost thou know who made thee,

Little lamb, I'll tell thee;
    Little lamb, I'll tell thee:
He is calléd by thy name,
For He calls Himself a lamb.
He is meek, and He is mild;
He became a little child:
I a child, and thou a lamb,
We are calléd by His name.
    Little lamb, God bless thee!
    Little lamb, God bless thee!

WILLIAM BLAKE

Badgers

Badgers come creeping from dark under ground,
Badgers scratch hard with a bristly sound,
Badgers go nosing around.

Badgers have whiskers and black and white faces,
Badger cubs scramble and scrap and run races,
Badgers like overgrown places.

Badgers don't jump when a vixen screams,
Badgers drink quietly from moonshiny streams,
Badgers dig holes in our dreams.

Badgers are working while you and I sleep,
Pushing their tunnels down twisting and steep,
Badgers have secrets to keep.

RICHARD EDWARDS

My Mother Saw a Dancing Bear

My mother saw a dancing bear
By the schoolyard, a day in June.
The keeper stood with chain and bar
And whistle-pipe, and played a tune.

And Bruin lifted up its head
And lifted up its dusty feet,
And all the children laughed to see
It caper in the summer heat.

They watched as for the Queen it died.
They watched it march. They watched it halt.
They heard the keeper as he cried,
"Now, roly-poly! Somersault!"

And then, my mother said, there came
The keeper with a begging-cup,
The bear with burning coat of fur,
Shaming the laughter to a stop.

They paid a penny for the dance,
But what they saw was not the show;
Only, in Bruin's aching eyes,
Far-distant forests, and the snow.

CHARLES CAUSLEY

At Home

The Country Bedroom

My room's a square and candle-lighted boat,
In the surrounding depths of night afloat.
My windows are the portholes, and the seas
The sound of rain on the dark apple-trees.

Sea monster-like beneath, an old horse blows
A snort of darkness from his sleeping nose,
Below, among drowned daisies. Far off, hark!
Far off one owl amidst the waves of dark.

FRANCES CORNFORD

Cats

Cats sleep
Anywhere,
Any table,
Any chair,
Top of piano,
Window-ledge,
In the middle,
On the edge,
Open drawer,
Empty shoe,
Anybody's
Lap will do,
Fitted in a
Cardboard box,
In the cupboard
With your frocks—
Anywhere!
They don't care!
Cats sleep
Anywhere.

ELEANOR FARJEON

At Home

Goldfish

the scene of the crime
was a goldfish bowl
goldfish were kept
in the bowl at the time:

that was the scene
and that was the crime

ALAN JACKSON

Houses

I like old houses best, don't you?
They never go cluttering up a view
With roofs too red and paint too new,
With doors too green and blinds too blue!
The old ones look as if they *grew,*
Their bricks may be dingy, their clapboards askew
From sitting so many seasons through,
But they've learned in a hundred years or two
Not to go cluttering up a view!

RACHEL FIELD

I Remember, I Remember

I remember, I remember
The house where I was born,
The little window where the sun
Came peeping in at morn;
He never came a wink too soon
Nor brought too long a day;
But now, I often wish the night
Had borne my breath away.

I remember, I remember
The roses, red and white,
The violets, and the lily-cups—
Those flowers made of light!
The lilacs where the robin built,
And where my brother set
The laburnum on his birthday—
The tree is living yet!

I remember, I remember
Where I was used to swing,
And thought the air must rush as fresh
To swallows on the wing;
My spirit flew in feathers then
That is so heavy now,
The summer pools could hardly cool
The fever on my brow.

At Home

I remember, I remember
The fir-trees dark and high;
I used to think their slender tops
Were close against the sky:
It was a childish ignorance,
But now 'tis little joy
To know I'm farther off from Heaven
Than when I was a boy.

Thomas Hood

The Swing

The garden-swing at the lawn's edge
Is hung beneath the hawthorn-hedge;
White branches droop above, and shed
Their petals on the swinger's head.
Here, now the day is almost done,
And leaves are pierced by the last sun,
I sit where hawthorn-breezes creep
Round me, and swing the hours to sleep:
Swinging alone—
By myself alone—
Alone,
Alone,
Alone.

At Home

In a soft shower the hawthorn-flakes descend.
Dusk falls at last. The dark-leaved branches bend
Earthward. . .The longest dream must have an end.

Now in my bedroom half-undressed,
My face against the window pressed,
I see once more the things which day
Gave me, and darkness takes away:
The garden-path still dimly white,
The lawn, the flower-beds sunk in night,
And, brushed by some uncertain breeze,
A ghostly swing beneath ghostly trees:
Swinging alone—
By itself alone—
Alone,
Alone,
Alone.

Eleanor Farjeon

INDEX

Introduction	Jane Asher	5
Ode to the Ozone	Hugh Tallents	6

THE SEASONS

Four Seasons	Anon	8
The Months	Sara Coleridge	8
Spring Song	Robert Browning	10
The Corn Growing	Leonard Clark	10
Written in March	William Wordsworth	11
The Scarecrow	Walter de la Mare	12
Adlestrop	Edward Thomas	13
September	Helen Hunt Jackson	14
Snow	Alice Wilkins	14
Stopping by Woods on a Snowy Evening	Robert Frost	15

THE EARTH

The Poem	Amy Lowell	17
Under Ground	James Reeves	18
Nettles	Vernon Scannell	19
Stupidity Street	Ralph Hodgson	20
Trees	Sara Coleridge	20
The Way through the Woods	Rudyard Kipling	21
Wood-Strawberries	Rachel Field	22
New Road	Leonard Clark	23

THE SEA AND THE SHORE

The Distance	Eleanor Farjeon	24
Neither Out Far Nor In Deep	Robert Frost	26
The Tides to me, The Tides to me	George Barker	27
The Great Blue Whale	Francesca Dimpfl	28
Echoes	Walter de la Mare	29

THE HEAVENS

Windy Nights	Robert Louis Stevenson	31
Storm	Roger McGough	32
Rain	Spike Milligan	33
The Weather	Gavin Ewart	33
The Stars at Night	Jane Taylor	34
Silver	Walter de la Mare	35
The Budgie	Stanley Cook	36
Three Owls	Richard Edwards	37
The Swallow	Christina Rossetti	37

SPIDERS AND FLIES AND MORE BESIDES

The Fly	William Blake	39
Upside Down	Aileen Fisher	40
Centipede	Anon	40
The Tickle Rhyme	Ian Serraillier	41
The Butterfly in Church	William Cowper	41
Silverfish, Spiders and Flies	Stanley Cook	42
If You Should Meet a Crocodile	Anon	43
Snake Glides	Keith Bosley	44

ANIMALS LARGE AND SMALL

Pussy	Anon	46
Mice	Rose Fyleman	47
Dappled Grey	Anon	48
The Cow	Robert Louis Stevenson	48
Ducks' Ditty	Kenneth Grahame	49
Prayers	Leonard Clark	50
The Lamb	William Blake	51
Badgers	Richard Edwards	52
My Mother Saw a Dancing Bear	Charles Causley	53

AT HOME

The Country Bedroom	Frances Cornford	55
Cats	Eleanor Farjeon	56
Goldfish	Alan Jackson	57
Houses	Rachel Field	57
I Remember, I Remember	Thomas Hood	58
The Swing	Eleanor Farjeon	60